# Getting Along With People You Love:

*Building and
Maintaining
Healthy
Relationships*

# MARILYN MORAVEC

David C. Cook Publishing Co.
Elgin, Illinois • Weston, Ontario

*Getting Along With People You Love: Building and Maintaining Healthy Relationships*
© 1989 by David C. Cook Publishing Co.
Originally published by Harvest Publications, Baptist General Conference.

David C. Cook Publishing Co.
850 North Grove Avenue
Elgin, IL 60120
Printed in U.S.A.

Editor: Gary Wilde
Cover and interior design: Ron Kadrmas
Interior illustrations: Terry Julien

ISBN: 1-55513-195-6
Library of Congress Catalog Number: 88-63883

# TABLE OF CONTENTS

◆

# BEFORE YOU BEGIN

This introductory chapter will help you understand some important facts so that you can use this book more effectively: why this topic; why this method; how to use this book; and how to facilitate the small group as you use this material.

## Why This Topic

I'm not going to waste time listing the statistics on what a mess the relationships all around us are. Nor am I going to depress you by quoting the current statistics on divorce. That is another issue. But I do want to call your attention to the relationships in the church, among the people of God. What do you think the surveys show about those?

I served on our denomination's Commission on Pastor/Church Relationships. For some time, I have been hearing about problems in churches as I've spoken around the country. And I've been deeply and sadly affected by what I learned as we researched what is happening in our churches. I also wrote to about fifteen other denominations and discovered that they were having the same problems: conflict, division, ineffectiveness in outreach.

I believe one of the greatest hindrances to what the Lord wants to do through us is our inability to love one another as He has loved us. It is through our unique, loving relationships that we are to draw people to God, to let them see we are disciples of Christ. In a world where a healthy relationship is rare, we are to be a light of hope that it can be done. We can love one another.

The families, marriages, and other relationships of those in Christian work are under tremendous stress. I serve on the National Association of Evangelicals' Task Force on the Family. The main goal is to promote family life education in the church. What we are discovering is that one big reason pastors are not doing much teaching on marriage and family life is because they are hurting in their own homes.

We all need help in our relationships. Learning to communicate, to listen, to understand, to handle conflict fairly, to forgive: These are all so difficult for us.

So I've elected to do a book that deals with some of the tension producers in relationships. Based on my experience in working with adults from many backgrounds, I've found these to be almost universal weak spots in the way we relate to others.

You'll find many people around you interested in improving their relationships. David Grant, author and lecturer, did research among sales people, managers, and other professionals, including those in education and religion. To the question, "What do you want most out of life?" the answer given most frequently was "A good relationship." It shouldn't be difficult to fill your group with interested people!

It is my vision that God will use this material to move us beyond mere problem solving to reaching a lost world.

## Why the Small Group Method

I love small groups. I believe in small groups. A small group can become an oasis where a person in need can retreat, get some needs met, and then go back to life's problems strengthened and helped. A Gallup poll taken in a large Protestant denomination revealed that for 52 percent of the people the small group was the support system for their faith.

I believe that if the churches I've seen go through terrible and destructive conflict had had a strong small-group ministry, much of that destruction could have been averted. Church growth consultant Lyle Schaller has said, "To a significant degree the strength and vitality of every congregation reflects the health of group life."

Every church experiences disruptive events: problems over a building program, disagreements over decisions, revelations of immorality, and so many more. The stronger the group life, the less likely a disruptive incident will have a long-term negative effect. Schaller asserts that a church is better able to handle disruptive events if it has a strong small group life. That makes sense. Disruptive events bring feelings, and feelings need to be processed. The healthy small group is an ideal place to deal with negative feelings. It's safe, its relationships are trusting, and if the Scriptures and prayer have been central to the times together, the Lord will have the freedom to correct thinking and attitudes.

And what better place to assimilate new people and to share with neighbors and friends the life that Christ gives us? It has been said that about 40-70 percent of new people are assimilated into the church by small groups, often at a time when they need added support to deal with a challenging life situation.

Most people become Christians at times of radical change in their lives. One survey revealed that 50 percent of believers have come to Christ during a personal crisis. I think that the percentage is actually higher. The small group can offer understanding, support, and spiritual resources for meeting human needs.

So many people you and I know are admittedly in pain over their relationships and their personal lives.

The material in this *Growing Together* series is ideal for a small group where you can invite friends and neighbors to your home or your church—or to the free room in your local bank—for a discussion. It can even be used on your lunch hour at work for a weekly meeting while you eat. The goal of a successful relationship or improving self-esteem motivates nearly everyone.

In addition to the reasons above, my prime motivation for putting this material into a small group format is that there is no better place to get know yourself than with a group of others who are interested in learning the same things. You can practice listening, caring, handling conflict, supporting, and confronting in your group. It's ideal. I trust you'll have a good time learning and growing together.

◆

# HOW TO USE THIS BOOK

## Size of Group

The ideal way to use this book is in a group of 2 to 12 people. A married couple or two friends can find it a wonderful experience for growing together. It can also be used for personal quiet time, though the benefit of interaction is lost.

If you're using it in a large group, break into small groups of 8-10 and stay with those people every time you meet.

## How Often?

It's important that you meet together regularly to interact over the material, the ideal being weekly. However, some groups have used the materials in monthly meetings and have found that the arrangement worked for them. Biweekly meetings are also feasible. A section can also be used at a retreat or church leadership meeting.

## Group Composition

Groups can be homogeneous, such as all women, all men, all couples, all singles, all elders, etc. Groups can also be mixed, made up of various ages, backgrounds, both sexes, of various marital status, those who know the Bible and those who don't. The target group is *adults open to growth*.

Leaders, such as a church staff, deacon board, women's or men's ministry boards, could profit greatly by using this material. One of the greatest challenges in lay and full-time ministry is maintaining healthy relationships. Using this material together should lead to excellent enrichment as well as an opportunity for problem-solving. The material is designed to build the relationships within the group using it.

Several chapters could be selected for use in a retreat setting. I've used small groups as the main vehicle of instruction at a retreat with no speaker and it was very effective. This would be especially functional for a small church or for the leadership of a large church.

## Special Numbering

Notice that the question numbers function primarily as thematic section markers. Thus, not all questions are numbered. For instance, number one may give a paragraph or two of informational material before actually raising a question to be answered in the blank space. Then there may be two or three more follow-up questions without numbers—since those questions still relate to the idea or theme in number one.

## Time Allotment

The book can be used in a variety of time frames. Adapt it to your needs. If you do each chapter at one sitting, you'll need about an hour and a half. If your group members are well acquainted, perhaps having done other books together, you may want to schedule two hours because the deepened relationships mean more sharing and therefore more time.

For 50-60 minute sessions, such as those in a Sunday School setting, do one half of a chapter per class session. The stopping point in each chapter will be indicated by this symbol:

---◆---

## Thirteenth Week Review (Optional):

1. Ask six volunteers (at least one week in advance) to each give a five-minute summary of one of the chapters.

2. Discuss together: "Which of the six concepts or chapters do you think is the most needed among Christians today? Why?"

3. Go around your group, each of you sharing which of the six chapters was the most meaningful to you and why.

4. Go around again and complete this sentence: "One improvement I've made in my life because of my involvement in this group has been...."

5. Go around again, each completing this sentence: "One thing I saw I need to work on but am still struggling with is ...."

6. Spend the rest of the time praying together, with sentence prayers, specifically for the needs you just shared.

## What Is a Facilitator?

This material is designed to be led by a facilitator, not a leader or teacher. The material itself will guide you through the study session. The word "facilitate" means "to make easier." The most important function of a facilitator is to help create an atmosphere of openness, warmth, and acceptance of one another. This will assist the process of personal growth for each group member, as well as deepen your fellowship. The main asset of the facilitator is his or her own life and desire to change and grow. The facilitator is a fellow member of the group with his or her own needs, who has the additional responsibility of keeping the group on target and watching the time.

One of the main challenges for the facilitator will be to help both the "overtalkers" and the "undertalkers" move toward healthy participation in the group discussions. Periodically challenge the group as a whole to move toward change by telling them: "Quiet people push yourself to share; those who share easily, discipline yourself to spend more time listening."

Occasionally you will have someone in the group with great needs. It's best that these be met outside the group time. Make arrangements to meet that person for coffee later so you can hear and respond to those needs. The responsibility of the facilitator is to keep a balance between meeting individual needs and making sure each lesson is covered. Pray for wisdom! When the discussion has slid into a tangent, it's best to take charge, and tell the group, "We need to get back to the book." Also, remember to contact absentees with a note or phone call before the next meeting.

The first lesson can be done without previous reading. If you elect to give out the books before the first meeting, be sure everyone has one. For some to have read the materials and not others is a poor beginning. If you have people who are not familiar with the Scriptures (and I hope you do), provide Bibles and use page numbers to make it easier for them to find the passages. Inexpensive Bibles are available through the Bible societies. It would be helpful for you to have Gospel booklets available for lesson six. You can obtain those in advance—see page xiv for addresses.

## How to Facilitate the Group

The most important thing to know about facilitating the *Growing Together* lessons is that *the material itself guides you through the group time.* Because of this, advance preparation by the group members can be helpful, but is not required. Therefore you can proceed with one of two options:

- Advance preparation option: You can encourage your group members to fill in their lesson before the meeting. Then, when they come to the group, you can zero in on key portions of the text or questions they want to deal with.
- No advance preparation option: I've found that in our busy day, many people will not do the lesson in advance. But with these lessons, that's okay.

**Instructions to the group and/or facilitator are placed within the material itself—in bold type, and indented on both sides.**

*You can read through the lesson aloud and answer the questions as you come to them. The study questions are designed in such a way that they can be answered as you move through the material together.*

The Icebreaker Ideas at the beginning of each chapter are optional, depending on the needs of your group. These activities are designed to get group members interacting in non-threatening ways. Some directly relate to that week's material, others are designed simply to loosen things up. Choose the ones that you are comfortable with and feel free to skip (or change) those that you don't think will work in your group.

Begin the group by reading the material aloud, or by asking a volunteer to do so. *As you work through each lesson, have every section and all Scriptures read aloud by volunteers.*

Do not call on anyone to read or share. All sharing should be voluntary. You'll discover that quiet people can be great growers. Verbal ability is not necessarily a sign of life change. Do not try to force openness. Instead, model it. On the questions where the instruction is given to go around the group, begin yourself and share in a way that will encourage others to follow your lead. This means you must be willing to be candid, open, and vulnerable. This is scary, but worth it in terms of helping the group move toward deeper levels of relating.

Most sessions end in group prayer. Do not go around the group for this. Allow those who wish to just listen to be comfortable, and those who wish to pray aloud to do so. Explain that sentence prayer is best in small groups; encourage simply talking to the Lord. Close the prayer time yourself or ask for a volunteer to close.

Prepare to facilitate the group by filling in your material thoroughly ahead of time. The other most important preparation is prayer. Pray specifically for each person in your group as well as for yourself, that God will be free to accomplish His goals in each of your lives.

## Some Additional Resources

### Bibles at excellent prices:

International Bible Society
144 Tices Lane
East Brunswick, NJ 08816

American Bible Society
1865 Broadway
New York, NY 10023

### Booklets explaining the Gospel:

*How to Have a Happy and Meaningful Life*
Dallas Theological Seminary
3909 Swiss Avenue
Dallas, TX 75204

*The Four Spiritual Laws*
Campus Crusade for Christ International
Arrowhead Springs
San Bernardino, CA 92414

*Steps to Peace With God*
Billy Graham Evangelistic Association
Box 779
Minneapolis, MN 55440

# Bibliography

General Relationships:
*The Friendship Factor,* Alan Loy McGinnis (Augsburg)

Marriage:
*Marriage Takes More Than Love,* Jack and Carole May-hall (Navigators)

Communication:
*Just Talk To Me,* Andre Bustanoby (Zondervan)

Spiritual Power in Relationships:
*Out of Solitude,* Henri J.M. Nouwen (Ave Maria Press)

*Restoring Your Spiritual Passion,* Gordon MacDonald (Thomas Nelson)

# 1. The Tension Producers

*Icebreaker Idea: Participants silently write answers to the completion sentences below, then have a volunteer read aloud the introductory material that follows.*

*My favorite way to spend leisure time is:*

*One thing that causes tension in relationships is:*

*One thing I hope to learn from this study is:*

1

**For each lesson in this book, start your group study time by reading aloud the introductory material that begins each chapter. As you work through the lesson, have every section and all Scriptures read aloud by volunteers.**

**R**ecently, I was having lunch in a restaurant and staring off into space. I like to get away from my office, alone, occasionally. I enjoy the solitude. As I ate, a conversation behind me caught my attention. I thought about turning to see the talkers when they left, but forgot to. But it doesn't matter what they looked like, because it could have been anyone who made this woman's surprising confession.

"I don't know what's worse—to be alone, or to fight with somebody," she declared.

I chuckled under my breath, but then a sadness came over me. Her honest disclosure is wrenchingly true. We don't want to be alone. In fact, we can't be. God made us to live best in the context of relationships. And yet, most of us can't make our relationships work, at least not the way we would like them to.

If we're honest we must all admit that relationships are a challenge, occasionally a hassle. Sometimes it takes only a word to develop a tension, even with people we love a great deal. This is true even in the church. And yet, Jesus declared that it is by the way we relate to each other that those around us will know that we are His disciples. And so we know that we must make an effort to learn to relate in love, to deal with our tensions and to come to harmony.

It is not easy. I discovered years ago that I needed some help with my own relationships. I found I lacked some of the basic skills, such as communication, working through conflict, and developing self-understanding, to name a few. It's been a long haul, and I don't have to tell you there are still moments when I can't figure out how I misunderstood my friend or neighbor. I've learned, though, that there are certain behaviors and attitudes on my part that will almost certainly cause tension in myself and eventually in the relationship. There are some clear cause-and-effect connections. Though it's been painful to see them, it's been a liberating discovery.

I've also seen unbelievable conflicts between the most godly people, across the kitchen table and the communion table. Something has got to be done. We can't reach a world that's in conflict when we are fighting among ourselves.

I'm convinced there are some answers. Of course, they're easier said than done. But if you're willing to work through these pages and then put what you learn into action, I know some of the tensions which may occur in your relationships will diminish, and in some cases disappear.

**Let's begin by getting better acquainted. Everyone share how they heard about this group. If you have been meeting together for some time, share one thing you appreciate about this group.**

**Now pair up; if there is an uneven number of people in the group, one "pair" can include three people. Share your answers to the Icebreaker Idea questions with your partner. You will be introducing your partner to the group in a moment, so listen well!**

**Now reassemble in your entire group. Go around, each person sharing what was learned about his or her partner. Give the name and at least one thing you learned about that person.**

**You've discussed with your partner what you think are some tension-producers in relation-**

3

ships. **Let's talk about that in the group. Together, compile a list of some things you believe cause people to be at odds with one another.**

1. What are some ways that tension in relationships shows itself?

2. In what specific ways do you think tension affects the following relationships? (For example, in friendship, unresolved tension can cause a lack of trust, so that the friends do not share openly with one another.)

   a. Friendship

   b. Marriage

   c. Fellow workers on the job

   d. Church relationships

3. What do you think are potential tension-producers in a small group such as ours?

4. The Book of Proverbs has a lot to say about tension in relationships. Look up the following verses from Proverbs 17 and share what you think they are saying about tension.

■ verse 1:


■ verse 9:


■ verse 10:


■ verse 14:


■ verse 17:


■ verse 19:


■ verse 27:


5. This book is about improving your relationships by reducing tension-producers. Here are some situations which illustrate the specific subjects we'll be talking about.

### Have three volunteers read these mini-cases aloud.

***Situation #1** Tension Producer: Lack of Directness*

Al has worked for the company for 26 years. In the last two months he has repeatedly had to work overtime.

He is the only one in his department who has been told he needs to stay late, though he has one of the longest tenures for the company. Anyone in the department could do what he is doing when he stays late. Al is getting tension headaches because he feels very angry about this injustice.

### *Situation #2 Tension Producer: Misperception in Communication*

Mr. Swanson lost his wife three months ago. He had sold his business to retire a year before she was diagnosed with cancer. Now he is experiencing the loss of his life work and his wife. People at church have noticed that he is irritable and touchy. He was recently elected the treasurer of the church. He has just stopped by the church office to pick up the books. In handing him the financial records, the secretary asks, "Mr. Swanson, do you type?"

"Of course I type; how do you think I got through 37 years of my own business? Just because I don't have a college education doesn't mean I can't handle things on my own."

The church secretary is devastated at Mr. Swanson's tirade, triggered by her question with which she was going to volunteer to do his typing.

### *Situation #3 Tension Producer: Unverbalized Expectations*

Karen and Tom have been married for four months. Karen has a terrible case of the flu and so has stayed home from work. She's been home all day alone; no phone calls or visitors. She feels neglected and unloved in her vulnerable state of not feeling well and having received no special attention in her need. When Tom comes home she rolls over and refuses to communicate with him.

For a while he thinks she's asleep and goes about his business starting his supper. He returns periodically to check on Karen. Finally he realizes she's awake, but cold toward him. He asks her what is wrong. She says, ''Nothing.''

Go back and look at the three situations above. In situation #1, I think Al needs to talk directly to his supervisor to find out what is happening here. He needs to be direct. What do you think the secretary in situation #2 needs to do? Is there any other action that needs to be taken in this situation? (Don't worry if you can't think of any answers; they will be covered in chapters ahead.)

Why, in situation #3, didn't Tom call all day? What is causing the tension here?

Now you have a taste of some of the tension-producers we'll be talking about in the weeks to come. I hope it whetted your appetite.

**Spend some time in your group sharing your reactions/insights/questions relating to the material you have studied so far.**

---

### God Sets the Standard

6. Let's shift our focus a bit. We want now to think about God's will for our relationships. Describe a relationship between two people that would delight God. What does He want our relationships to be like?

**Have each Scripture below read aloud, then write down the ways of relating that God commands after each passage is read:**

- Romans 13:8-10

- Romans 14:19

- I Corinthians 13:4-7

- Colossians 3:12-14

- James 1:19, 20

- I John 4:7, 11, 12

Now that you've seen some of God's instructions for our relationships, how do you feel? (I must admit I feel overwhelmed after reading these verses. God's standard is very high. Certainly we cannot live this way without the power and love of the Spirit of God filling us.)

**Read James 3:16-18.**

7. William Barclay comments on this passage: "Nothing good can ever grow in an atmosphere where men [and women] are at variance with one another."[1]

In verse 16, what grows out of envy and selfish ambition?

What are some modern-day examples of "disorder and every evil practice" in the church?

In the home?

The "peace" in verse 18 is literally "right relationships between man and man."[2] How do you think good or "righteousness" (acting rightly, according to God's standards) can spring out of right relationships between people?

What specific kinds of "good" grow in that kind of atmosphere?

### Read John 13:34, 35.

8. How does the way that we relate to one another affect our witness of what our God is like?

As you close your time together today, talk for a few moments about what your expectations are for this discussion group and for this material. Share your expectations together.

As a group, spend a few moments in spontaneous sentence prayers, with those who wish to do so praying out loud. Your facilitator will close in prayer.

For next week, fill in the answers to the questions in chapter 2. By preparing in advance you'll get the maximum benefit from your group discussion time.

[1]Barclay, William, *The Letters of James and Peter,* Revised Edition (Philadelphia: Westminster Press, 1976), page 97.
[2]Barclay, page 97.

# 2. The Power of Misperception

*Icebreaker Idea: On a separate sheet of paper, have each person draw a simple self portrait (face only). After a couple of minutes, your facilitator should collect the papers, shuffle them, assign each a number, and have everyone guess who's who.*

The air was chilling even though it was just September. I guess Minnesota is like that. My friend and I were driving home from Trout Lake Camp and Retreat Center, where I had just given a series of messages on communication. The temperature in the car was dropping by the minute. Lynn reached for the heater button. After

11

about ten minutes and no heat, we realized it wasn't working, so we pulled into the nearest gas station. We told the attendant our problem, then headed for the waiting room.

It was definitely sparse, one chair and no coffee pot. Lynn sat down; the whole chair moved from side to side. "It's a good thing *you* didn't sit here," she said to me.

At that time I was chubbier than Lynn, and I had been trying to cut my calories. My spontaneous thought was, "Well, I'm not that much heavier than she is." You see, what I heard her say was, "It's a good thing you didn't sit here, because you'd probably fall down since this chair is so rickety—and you're heavier than I am." I felt irritated. But I had just spoken on the glories of good listening. So I caught myself before I could tell her she had a lot of nerve saying a thing like that. Instead, I fed back what I thought she was saying, "Are you saying I'm too heavy for that chair?"

The shocked look on her face told me I was being ridiculous. She answered, "No, I was saying this chair would be bad for your back." (I'd recently been suffering with a backache.)

Now don't tell me you've never jumped to a negative conclusion as I did. And chances are you didn't check out the meaning, so you stayed angry or hurt. I believe this kind of misperception happens regularly in human relationships. It is true that some people are more prone to misinterpret, but we all do it at times. I had been focusing on my weight, which is what led to my false conclusion. When we have something on our minds about ourselves, we're likely to imagine an attack or put-down where there simply isn't one.

Remember the situation in chapter one between Mr. Swanson and the church secretary? A fellow church staff member told me about this experience. It happened exactly as I recounted it for you. These kinds of misperceptions happen in the church, on the job, and in friendships, but they also occur in the closest of relationships in the home. Sometimes we're most vulnerable to misreading a look, a comment, or a lack of time or attention or touch from someone close to us, because we need that person's love and respect so much. The destruction caused by such misperceptions can be disastrous.

In John 8:44, Satan is described as the father of lies. Could we not unknowingly open ourselves to his influence in these areas? Often, when we're not communicating, we have anger stuck inside. In addition, we're not allowing God free reign in our thought life. Thus, we're certainly vulnerable to other influences and temptations—all because we do not deal with the misperceptions, and the anger and unrealistic attitudes that can begin to flow from them.

1. What is your response to my experience with my friend, Lynn? When have you had a similar experience?


Look back at situation #2 in chapter one (page 6). How did you interpret or react to Mr. Swanson's outburst?


**Read Ephesians 4:25-27 in as many different translations as you have available.**

2. Let's see how the Bible says misperceptions can lead to anger. What does the passage say we're to do?


What are we *not* to do?

What does it mean to you to "let the sun go down while you are still angry?"

Which is easier to do for you: "Sweeping it under the rug," or talking directly? Why?

What are the results of allowing anger to grow without checking the truth or falsehood of our perceptions?

How do you think undealt-with anger "gives the devil an opportunity"? How, specifically, do you think Satan could work when we have anger stuck inside of us?

**Read James 1:19, 20 in several translations.**

3. Write the three commands given in these verses in your own words.

What is the result of giving a verbal response before you've really listened?

How do you believe God feels about that?

## Read Proverbs 18:13.

4. Write this proverb in your own words.




**Discuss in your group: What does it mean to you to "answer before listening"? What are some ways that could happen in this group?**

---

### Learn To Be Direct

5. Below are several situations. Write a statement in the spaces provided telling what you think the speaker means.

Charlie's boss, Mr. Kenton, approaches Charlie's desk and says, "Oh, you're going to do *that* first?"



Alice to Ken, the choir director: "I notice you're using a lot of contemporary music lately."



Jean to her husband Jim: "Do you have to do all that tonight?"



Cal is sitting at the kitchen table looking through the bills for the month. To his wife Sue, he says, "I can't believe this bill of $20.00 for Bobbie's shoes."

15

Listed below are the actual meanings in the minds of the speakers.

Mr. Kenton: "I need you to make *this* a priority. Would you do it first please?"

Alice: "You're the first choir director we've ever had that used contemporary music, and I'm thrilled."

Jean: "I'd like to go to my mom's later; could you plan to do less tonight?"

Cal: "When I look through these bills and see how much money we need every month, I feel so inadequate; I wish I could bring in more money."

**As a group, compare what you thought the speaker was saying with the actual meaning.**

What do you learn about misperceptions here?



How common do you think these kinds of misunderstandings are?



What should the speaker do to prevent misunderstanding?



What kind of tension are these misunderstandings capable of producing in relationships?



6. How could misperceptions on the part of the hearers be prevented in each of these situations? Go back over each of the four above and write down what the hearer

could say in order to clarify the speaker's meaning. I've filled in one as an example.

Charlie to Mr. Kenton:

Ken to Alice: "Are you pleased or displeased with my using a lot of contemporary music?"

Jim to Jean:

Sue to Cal:

7. Notice from the four situations how often people will use a question instead of stating their thoughts, feelings, or requests directly. Why do you think we do that?

What do you think is God's way of dealing with people? What kind of example did Jesus give us in stating our thoughts and feelings—directness or indirectness? (See John 4:16; 5:6 and 8:49 as examples.)

When you think of being direct (making yourself clear, saying up front what you mean), what does it feel like to you? Is it scary and uncomfortable, safe and pleasant, somewhere in between? Explain.

To what extent do you view directness as abrupt or unkind?

**Discuss and evaluate what directness means to you.**

**Have someone reread Ephesians 4:25-27.**

How does this passage apply?

8. A well-known expert on the family, Virginia Satir, has said, "As a therapist, I have found that the more indirectly people communicate, the less healthy their relationships will be."

What do you think she means?

How does this apply to the family of God? (See Ephesians 4:25 again; "members of one body.")

**Summarize in your own words what you have learned about the power of misperception in relationships.**

**Close your time together with a brief period of spontaneous sentence prayers, praying aloud if you wish to do so. Pray specifically for yourself about what we've talked about today.**

# 3. "Well, What Do You Expect?"

*Icebreaker Idea: Break your group into pairs. One person think of something you want your partner to do (eg., shut the door, move a chair, smile). Then allow one minute for the "communicator" to get this message across **without speaking**—using only his or her feet and elbows to communicate!*

*After this exercise, share: How did it go? Who was able to communicate with his partner? Why was this so hard? Share a time when you expected someone to know what you were thinking, or needed, without having to tell them. Describe the circumstances and tell what happened.*

Two phone calls within the last half hour, each wanting to know if there would be a bus for the social that night. I had to admit I didn't know. "Just come," I told the callers, "if there's no bus, we'll carpool." I couldn't believe Al never let me know. I assumed he would call me back to let me know what he'd decided, since I am ultimately responsible for the finances of our group.

Wouldn't you think he'd know I needed to be informed? We had talked earlier in the week about the evening's activity. We talked about the pros and cons of a bus. I assumed that after he made the phone calls for more information, he'd call me back. I expected that, and when he hadn't done it I felt irritated. I had made an assumption. Was that fair?

Remember situation #3 in chapter one? Karen and Tom are a newly married couple. Karen is home sick and Tom doesn't call her all day. As a result, she withdraws when he comes home and is cold toward him the rest of the evening. She made an assumption. Growing up in her family, when you were sick you got lots of attention and "warm fuzzies." In his family, the way they showed love was to tiptoe around and give the person lots of quiet and rest; they viewed being alone without interruption as the road to wellness. Karen was crushed by what she perceived as a lack of love.

What we need is so clear in our minds that we cannot imagine that the other person does not know what we want. Is that fair? Is it a reasonable expectation to assume that the other person can know what we think they should do? Is it fair to assume that he or she will view his or her responsibility to us in the same way that we do? I realized later that Al handled the bus situation and didn't think it important to bother me with details. If my expectation was that he would inform me, I needed to ask him to call me back to let me know the results.

Unverbalized and sometimes unconscious expectations cause many misunderstandings, conflicts, and problems in relationships. It is this issue of expectations that we will discuss in this chapter.

**Go around your group making sure everyone knows each other's names. Now that you've completed two chapters, have you seen any changes in the way you relate to others? Share.**

**Discuss: What does the word "expectation" mean to you? Talk about what having expectations in a relationship means to you, and give some examples.**

1. Let's think about the expectations that affect various kinds of relationships. In each example below there is an unverbalized expectation. Under each example, write what you think that expectation is.

a. Choir director to Sue, who has been in choir for three months (this is the first time she missed a rehearsal): "Sue, I missed you Wednesday. I didn't know you wouldn't be there."

His unverbalized expectation:

b. Marcia and Alice have been friends for some time. Alice is taking a class two nights a week, so she's busier than she was before. Marcia calls Alice to go shopping Saturday, something they often have done before. Over the phone Alice says, "I can't go. I wish I could. I'll call you later. Good-bye." Marcia is hurt and angry.

Marcia's expectation:

Alice's expectation:

21

c. Craig and Judy have been married for 28 years. All the kids are launched, so Judy went back to work last year. She's done well and has already been promoted.

"Judy, the company Christmas party is next Saturday."

"I can't believe it, Craig, mine's the same night. We'll have to split the evening."

"Split the evening? Judy, you know that the party is always a dinner, and then the company awards. How can we leave? We've always had a good time. Why wouldn't you want to stay the evening?"

Craig's assumption and expectation:


Judy's expectation:


d. There is intense pressure at work right now, because of production deadlines. Rich has been in management for three years. He's never seen so much tension on the job. A lot of money is at stake in this deal. His boss, Jack, comes into his office and plops himself down on his couch.

"We're going to have to really push these people in the plant or we're not going to make the deadlines." Jack looks tense.

"I know. Cal stopped by. He said he met with the men last week to tell them about the big push."

"I don't think Cal said it hard enough. They need to hear it from a 'big gun'."

"Sounds like a good idea. Are you going to meet with them?" Rich views Jack as the person with the most clout.

"That's your responsibility. If we don't get this job done, you and a lot of other people will be jobless. You should have figured out that Cal isn't strong enough. Get on it right away." Jack leaves the room, slamming the door behind him.

Jack's expectation:

Rich's expectation:

e. Pastor Jones has been at the church for four months. Every morning when Vern passes the church at 8:00 a.m. on his way to work, he sees the secretary's car, but not the pastor's car. At 4:00 p.m. he passes again and often the pastor's car is absent. Vern is not involved in any committees or other evening activities, so he is unaware of the four evenings a week that Pastor Jones is at church, or the afternoons he spends at the hospital. Vern is wrestling with doubts about his pastor's work habits. "What kind of banker's hours does this man have? I work hard to give my tithe. Maybe I should cut back. Maybe it's not a good investment."

Vern's expectation of pastor:

Pastor's view of the congregation's expectation of him:

There are two kinds of relational problems above. First, there is the kind of conflict that comes simply from not understanding the other person's expectation, such as the one between Karen and Tom (from chapter one). Simply communicating would solve the problem. If Tom knew that Karen wanted to be called and that his call would not be an interruption of her rest, but rather a sign of caring, he would doubtless have called her. This kind of misunderstanding can be cleared up through communication.

The other kind of problem we see above is where the expectations are not only uncommunicated, but they conflict. This means that there needs to be communication *and then negotiation.* Negotiation and resolution cannot occur until the conflicting expectations are made clear.

**Can you recall any situations in your past experience in which direct communication and/or negotiation brought resolution? Share with the group.**

◆

**A** great deal of anger in many relationships is generated through unverbalized and sometimes conflicting expectations. As I stated earlier, what we need is so clear in our minds that we can't imagine that the other person does not know what we want. By not stating what we want—clearly and directly—we cause misperceptions of what we want. If both you and your partner or friend do this, both of you will be inclined to get angry about things you expect the other person to know you want.

We've looked at several situations so far (Al and me, Karen and Tom [from Chapter 1], choir director and Sue, Marcia and Alice, Craig and Judy, Rich and his boss). In which of these situations do you think clear communication of expectations would solve the problem?

In which of these situations do you think negotiation after communicating expectations would be necessary?

What do you think will happen in each of these situations if the persons do not communicate directly? Go through each and anticipate the probable results of "sweeping it under the rug."

Al and Marilyn:

Karen and Tom:

Choir director and Sue:

Marcia and Alice:

Craig and Judy:

Rich and his boss:

Go through each of these situations and write down what this person could say to the other person involved in order to understand one another's expectations. A couple are done for you.

Marilyn to Al: (This is the example at the beginning of this chapter.)

Karen to Tom: (Situation #3 in chapter 1)


Sue to choir director or choir director to Sue: (Sue could catch on that he wants to be informed and ask, "Do you like us to call you if we are going to miss choir?" This would make the expectation clear. Or the choir director could realize he hadn't verbalized that and do so.) What could he say? Either one could speak up so that this would not happen again.


Marcia to Alice: "I know your schedule has changed, but I assumed you would make time for our friendship."

Alice to Marcia: "I expected you to understand that things have to change now that I'm a lot busier. I have to study today. I still want to be friends, but we'll have to spend less time shopping for awhile."

Craig to Judy:


Judy to Craig:


Rich to Jack:


Jack to Rich:


Vern to Pastor Jones: (Since the pastor doesn't know of Vern's question, Vern would have to initiate this discussion.)

2. Can you see how hidden expectations affect relationships? Can you think of any examples in your life where this has caused problems?

For example, with grown children, how often do you expect them to call or visit? Is that a point of contention?

What are the expectations in your family regarding holidays and how they are spent? Has that ever caused conflict?

Any other examples, at home, at church, on the job, in friendships? Write down an example from your own experience, including your response.

3. What do you think is the Christian way to handle hidden expectations?

The way that God relates to us is the perfect model of relating. How clear are His expectations of us? (Silently skim these passages as examples: Matt. 5:5-15; 9:37, 38 and Mark 9:33-37.)

## Read Matthew 7:7, 8.

What does Jesus say to do when we have a need or want?




Although God knows our minds and knows our needs and wants before we ask Him, He tells us to ask. There is value in learning to articulate our needs and wants, even with the Lord. Though there is little direct biblical teaching on openness, the Bible teaches that we are to be honest with one another. Jesus knew what was in people and what they were thinking. The hidden thoughts and expectations that infect so many relationships and cause anger are not His way.

The alternatives to openness are giving up our expectations or developing resentment. Undoubtedly there are some expectations which should be given up because they're unrealistic, but there are many that we feel are legitimate.

In your opinion, what happens when we do not verbalize our legitimate expectations?




## Read Acts 5:3 and Mark 8:32, 33.

4. Apparently, Satan can be active in our relationships. (Ephesians 4:25-27 states that Satan gains power ["foothold"] in our lives when we harbor anger inside.) In both Scripture passages, we see the thinking of believers being influenced by Satan. When we are angry because people don't meet our expectations, what kinds of "poisonous thoughts" can develop in our minds?

How does talking to the person involved cut short those poisonous thoughts?

5. What are some reasons why we often do not talk directly to the person involved? What are some fears that we have?

6. What do you think is the difference between making a demand and sharing an expectation?

7. Are there any people right now that you've realized you need to tell what you need or want from them? This group can offer support as you work toward talking directly to that person.

**Together, summarize in your own words what you have learned about unverbalized expectations.**

**Spend the last few moments together in spontaneous sentence prayers, with those who wish to do so, praying aloud.**

# 4. We Want to Change Each Other

*Icebreaker Idea: Write down one of your "pet peeves" on a separate piece of paper. Maybe it's people's alarm watches sounding during church, or people cutting in front of you in line. The facilitator should collect these and read them. Try to guess who said what.*

*Discuss: Have you ever tried to get someone to stop an irritating habit? How did it go?*

Have you ever had someone close to you "working on you" to get you to change in some way? Most of us have experienced this. I believe there is some effort to change the other person in every relationship. We all seem to feel that our way is the best way and that we need to help the other person to live a better life. And aren't we supposed to motivate one another to righteousness? Is it really caring to accept the other person as he is and not be concerned that he's falling short of God's best for him? Shouldn't we be helping each other to change? Where is the line between being a superior busy-body and the loving confrontation that the Bible commands of us when we see a brother or sister in a sin? These kinds of questions are very important issues in the health of every relationship you have—those at home, at your job, and within your church.

The balance of accepting the other person and yet confronting when we ought to requires the leading of the Spirit of God. I believe He wants us to be more aware of the tension we produce in our relationships, and the destruction we allow because we do not understand His way of treating people. I believe that we're both meddling too much and not lovingly confronting enough. We're erring on both sides of the balance.

Let's deal first with the wrongful approach of trying to change the other person. (In the next chapter we'll look at confrontation.) I believe this tendency infests every relationship on earth. Interacting in a small group is an ideal way to learn more about relationships, because we'll be relating as we learn.

**We've completed half of our study together. What would you say are some of the most meaningful ideas that we've talked about? Go around the group, each answering.**

**In the introduction to this chapter, the phrase "someone working on you" is given. What**

does it feel like to you to have someone "working on you?" Go around the group again, each person naming one feeling he or she has when sensing that someone is trying to change him or her. Several of you may have the same one; just tell what you feel.

1. There is some effort to change the other person in almost every relationship. Why do you think we try to change the other person?

### Together, list as many reasons as you can think of.

How many of these reasons are desires to meet the need of the other person?

How many seem to be related to our own needs?

2. What effects have you noticed when you tried to change someone? (Apply this question in your mind to a specific change you desire in someone you work with, or someone at church, or someone close to you. What happens when you "work" on him or her?)

What response do you usually get?

There are generally three responses in a person or in the relationship when we try to change others against their will:

a. He will change to please you and be angry because he feels controlled. In other words, you've won. The other person gives in to your pressure, but because he is acting against his own free choice, he resents you. Therefore the relationship is impaired by underground anger. This anger is often revealed in illness, depression, irrational disagreements, coldness, sexual problems in marriage, parenting disagreements.

b. She will resist because of a power struggle that develops. Even if she begins to see that the change is desirable, she will not choose it because you and she are now in an adversarial stance, and she doesn't want you to "win."

c. The other person will do what you want when you're present and what he wants when you're not around. The relationship becomes infected with dishonesty.

Do any of these three feel familiar to you? Do you see one as the way you sometimes react or the way someone close to you reacts?

**Share some illustrations as you
think of them.**

**Take a moment now for silence in the group
as each of you answers the following question alone.**

3. List some things about yourself that others probably find disagreeable and wish you would change. List a few of these for each relationship below. To get you started, let me list a few of mine:

33

- My definition of "on time" is within 10 minutes of when I agreed to arrive.

- I am a pack rat. I save everything, especially papers. I have piles as well as files. My desk looks bad.

- I always squeeze the toothpaste in the middle of the tube.

- I spend a lot of money on books.

- I don't do my hair on my day off.

- The rust spots on my last car didn't bother me.

- Whatever I'm reading is always piled on the end tables and floor around my favorite easy chair, and I always have papers on my dining room table and my kitchen counter.

- I can get stubborn when I feel pushed.

- Though I talk a lot about listening, in close relationships I find my mind wandering to what I have to do. (This one I feel very badly about and am working on. Just wanted you to know that.)

- I drive abruptly, so that some of my passengers feel nervous.

Now list a few for each of your relationships.

Close Relationships: (Mate, close friend, family.)




Working Relationships: (If you are a full-time homemaker, use neighbors or friends here.)




Church Relationships:

**Spend a few minutes sharing whatever you would like to in your group from #3. What feelings do you have about your list?**

4. Do you find people trying to change these things about you? If so, what is your response? If not, how does it feel to be accepted in spite of your imperfections?

### Read Ephesians 2:8, 9.

What word is used to describe salvation? What does this tell you about God's method of accepting you through Christ?

There is a potent statement in the book *The Imitation of Christ*. It says, "Be not angry that you cannot make others as you wish them to be, since you cannot make yourself as you wish to be."[1] A great motivator for me in accepting the other person as he is is realizing what he has to put up with in me.

**Share in your group: What is your reaction to this quote?**

◆

## God Says Accept Each Other

**Read Romans 15:1-7. If you have several translations in the group, have the passage read in as many as possible.**

5. How does God view one person trying to change another person?

What do you think He thinks and feels as He sees us pressuring or manipulating other people? (Manipulation is trying to change the other person through subtle ways, such as making her feel guilty enough to do what we want her to do. Obviously, it's not honest and open.)

Differences are threatening to us. I'm convinced that that's what is behind many prejudices, whether of race, religion, or sex. We're plain scared of someone who is different from us, and our sinful nature distorts our thinking into the idea that our way is best. Our thinking goes: Anyone different from me is not as good—therefore I must change him. Stated that way it really sounds distasteful, doesn't it?

    Well, human nature was the same in the early church. Some of the differences that were prevalent then were in the areas of Christian liberty and Gentile privilege. But regardless of what disagreements are about, God tells us that He values harmony. What does the word "harmony" or "spirit of unity" in verse 5 mean to you?

Which meaning do you think is closer to what Paul meant: "be the same" or "accept the differences"?

What behaviors or attitudes are the opposite of "accepting the differences"? (Examples: criticism, judgments.)

## Read Ephesians 4:2, 3.

6. What does "bearing with one another" mean to you?

These passages help us to deal with any difference of viewpoint where, to the parties involved, both ways seem right before God (such as your way of handling money versus mine; your idea of what is appropriate to wear to a family dinner or mine; your idea of Christian life-style versus mine; your way of choosing an architect for the new building or mine; your way of keeping the church's financial records versus mine, etc.) What commands and guidelines are given us in these passages to deal with our differences? List them.

Which of these commands is hardest for you to obey?

What are some specific ways we can please our neighbor for his good and not just to please ourselves? Be specific.

The command is to accept one another as Christ has accepted us. How has Christ accepted you?

**Read Romans 5:6-8.**

7. What does it mean to you that Christ has accepted you unconditionally, in your weakness and in your sin?

What result does Romans 15:7 state will occur when we accept one another?

Have you thought about how we can "glorify God," "bring praise to God"? The way stated here is so painfully nitty-gritty, so everyday. What happens when we are not accepting one another?

**Read John 13:34, 35.**

8. What are people likely to think if we are not loving to one another?

Part of loving is accepting others as they are. How does the way we accept or don't accept others affect our witness?

> The command to "accept one another" is foundational to dealing with our differences as well as to glorifying God and having a powerful message to the world. To summarize, talk a little more about what you think it means to "accept" someone.

The Greek word used in Romans 15:7 for "accept" is *proslambano*. According to *Vine's Expository Dictionary of New Testament Words,* the word means you take the person to yourself or receive him, with a special interest, suggesting a welcome. Charles Sell, in his book *Achieving the Impossible—Intimate Marriage,* says that this word is the same one used for people taking food at a banquet. He describes reaching out for one another with the same vigor that we would use to reach for our favorite dish of Heavenly Hash chocolate ice cream (one of my favorites). We are to have a warm welcoming attitude toward others even though they are different from us.

**What's your response to this command of God? (Mine is: "Oh help, Lord.") Spend a moment in group quiet while each of you writes a brief letter to God in the space below, sharing whatever is on your heart with Him right now. Remember, He accepts you as you are right now.**

**Close your group with a time of brief sentence prayers about this issue of accepting others as they are. Those who would like to do so may pray.**

[1]àKempis, Thomas, *The Imitation of Christ* (New York: Grosset & Dunlap).

# 5. The Other Side Of Acceptance: Confrontation

*Icebreaker Idea: Who would be the hardest person in the world for you to confront with something wrong that they've done? Why?*

*(Consider asking for pairs of volunteers to roleplay situations of confronting this person. The group could then discuss insights about what factors help move confrontation toward conflict resolution.)*

Balance is very important in relationships. It is true that we are to accept one another, but does that mean we are to accept *everything?* Are we never to show displeasure or say "no" to another's behavior?

The life of the Lord Jesus tells us immediately that at times we should confront the other person. He was amazingly unaccepting at times, often with the Pharisees. There were times when He confronted His disciples as well. He didn't just let them go on, accepting their objectionable behavior. He always accepted people; He didn't always accept their actions or their attitudes.

Nor did the Lord walk away in rejection of them. There was a time when He told His disciples to leave the town where their message was rejected, but He never told them to reject anyone. He showed us the way to live and the way to love, by accepting other people, and when necessary, by confronting.

It is easy to confuse Christian acceptance of others with becoming passive, being afraid to face conflict, and not taking a stand for what is right. Passivity is not acceptance. Acceptance is a decision made from strength and love; passivity is a stance of fear. It is being afraid to object, rather than choosing to love.

1. Here are some examples of situations. Would "acceptance" of the person's behavior in any of these situations be passivity and fear of confrontation, or would it be loving? Circle the letter of the ones that would demand loving confrontation rather than acceptance. In the spaces provided, jot down some notes regarding the reasons for your choice.

**As your group reads through each situation below, discuss and/or debate the merits of either accepting or confronting.**

41

a. John is called upon consistently to work overtime without pay, while others in the same position are not.

b. Karen's husband has just come home with his new purchase of video equipment, even though they don't have enough money to pay the electric bill.

c. Sally's neighbor in the condominium blares music at 10:30 p.m.

d. Alice's boss directs sexual innuendos at her, which others in the office also interpret as sexual.

e. Nancy finds the socks as usual, on the floor just outside the hamper.

f. Jim and Cal are roommates, and they serve together on the C. E. board at their church. One day, while using Cal's car, Jim looks under the front seat for a cloth to clean the window. Instead, he finds a pornographic magazine under the driver's seat.

g. Mr. Jones comes up after the worship service, as he has nearly every Sunday for the last two months, and tells Carl, the new choir director, that he didn't like his selection of music.

h. Ken is near the front door waiting for his wife Shirley to be ready. She's 25 minutes late now and that's not unusual.

i. Greg enters the back door and sees the kitchen is just as it was when he left this morning. When he gets upstairs, he sees a painfully familiar sight. His wife Jan is laying on the bed, the half-drunk bottle of whiskey on the nightstand.

2.  What should each of these Christians do? I remember a book I read many years ago. Its impact never left me. Charles Sheldon, in his classic *In His Steps,* mandates that when you're trying to figure out how to handle a situation, you ask yourself, "What would Jesus do?" What do you think? How would He handle each situation above?

> **Talk about this. Select three or four of these situations (a through i above) that most interest you. Think of how Jesus would have responded. Share.**

3.  Can you think of any principles that would help you decide on whether to act and confront, or to accept and not do anything?

Later in this chapter we'll look at some Scriptures that will give us some principles.

4. God accepts us unconditionally in Christ. Does that mean that He never objects, is never grieved, or never corrects us? Of course not.

### Read these passages and then discuss what God does when we are out of line:

Ephesians 4:30. Here we see God, the Holy Spirit, responding to the behavior and attitudes of the Ephesians. To what is He reacting?

What is His response?

What does it mean to you that He is "grieved"?

Hebrews 12:5, 6. In the previous passage we saw the grief of the Spirit of God toward our sin. Here we see the action of the Father toward us when we sin. What does He do?

### Read verses 10, 11 in the same chapter.

For what purposes does God discipline us?

We see from these passages that unconditional acceptance is not passivity; in fact, it is the opposite, it cares enough to grieve, to confront, and to act.

There are basically two kinds of situations which we need to confront. The first situation occurs when

44

a relationship is impaired by what I am feeling about what the other person is doing toward me. I need to confront that person in order to achieve reconciliation and peace, as well as to support what I believe is justice in the situation. Secondly, when I see a fellow Christian doing something which is clearly sin, I need to confront. In the first situation, the confrontation is for the sake of myself and my feelings, which are affecting the relationship. We could say it is for the good of the relationship. In the second situation, it is for the good of the other person. In this chapter we'll talk about confronting for the good of the other person. (Note: If you are interested in learning more about confrontation for the sake of relationship, see my book *Living in Harmony: Facing Conflict in Relationships* in this *Growing Together* series.)

> **Discuss in your group: How do you feel about the idea of "confronting for myself"? Isn't this selfish? Why or why not?**

---

## Confronting for Righteousness

5. Look back over situations a through i on pages 42 and 43. In which do you think the confrontation is for the good of the other person, to help him or her live righteously? Ask yourself: Is a clear scriptural principle being violated here?

This is my opinion: Situations b, d, f, and i are situations where righteousness demands confrontation. The others have more to do with relationship, so communication to understand one another may be all that is necessary to solve the problem. Below are the examples of confrontations for righteousness:

b. Karen's husband needs to be confronted with his primary obligations. She needs to listen to him, as he may have some plans on how to pay the bills, but it looks as though he is violating a principle of first responsibility to family. It is Karen's obligation to find out more. It will help her to be honest about her feelings, and if he listens, she has helped their relationship and their financial situation. If he does not listen, she may decide to accept the situation and wait for him to handle the bills, or she may decide to ask for help from a counselor or pastor. What do you think?

**Read I Timothy 5:8. How does it apply here?**

d. Alice's boss is obviously violating her rights to be treated with dignity and respect. In my opinion, Alice needs to confront her boss in private and let him know she does not want to be treated that way. He may think his behavior is perfectly acceptable. She needs to tell him. What are the risks in telling him?

What are the risks in *not* telling him?

f. I believe Jim needs to confront Cal. He needs to share how disturbing it was to see the magazine in Cal's car. He needs to ask if the magazine is Cal's. If it is, he needs to ask what Cal's struggles are and do some good listening. After a time of empathy and support, I believe he needs to suggest to Cal that he get some professional or pastoral help with this problem, since it is a clear violation of Matthew 5:27, 28. While he is getting that help, he may need to resign from the C.E. board. If Cal says the magazine is not his, I still believe Jim needs to do some loving probing since it is difficult to understand why a Christian would keep a pornographic magazine in his car under any circumstances. What will happen if Jim "chickens out" and does not confront his roommate?

i. Jan's drinking is an obvious violation of scriptural principles, because it now controls her. See Ephesians 5:18 and I Corinthians 6:12. How do they apply?

I believe Greg needs to do something about Jan's drinking. I cannot imagine the Lord Jesus not doing something constructive to help Jan. She probably needs to be hospitalized. She would have to agree to this, but Greg can insist that he will not allow this to go on any longer. He will find it helpful to take action for himself, such as attending Al-Anon, an organization for family members of those with a drinking problem, which uses the same 12 steps as Alcoholics Anonymous. He may need the understanding, insight, and support provided there. Alcoholism does not just go away. It tends to get worse and worse. There is far more alcoholism among believers than anyone would like to admit. Action must be taken. Love demands it. What is your opinion?

6. Let's do one more exercise with these four situations. Go back and decide what exactly you would say to the person in each case, if you needed to do the confronting. Do not accuse. Share your feelings and con-

victions. A suggestion is given for one. Evaluate it and rephrase in your own words.

### Do this exercise aloud in your group.

b.

d. "Mr. Jones, I do not want you to speak to me with sexual innuendos, such as this morning when you said. . . . Please do not talk to me like that."

f.

i.

### Read Galatians 6:1, 2.

7. List three commands in this Scripture.

The Scripture above demands sensitive involvement in the lives of others. It is difficult to keep the balance. On which end do you tend to err: Minding your own business to the point of not confronting sin, or, insensitive confronting to the point of meddling?

**My guess is that many of us find it easier to be passive. We tend to ignore situations where there is obvious sin. Together, list as many reasons as you can think of for why we don't get involved.**

It costs something to get involved with the lives of others to the point of bearing their burdens, supporting them as they struggle with sin, and taking action if they refuse to turn away from sinful behavior. What does it cost us?

What do you think it costs the church and the individual when we refuse to correct each other?

I remember years ago at a church social, I caught a glimpse of one man's wife looking intently into the eyes of another woman's husband. It looked like an intimate conversation. I remember rebuking myself for thinking such a thing. About a year later, the woman came to me for help. She was in the midst of an affair with the man. The tragic end was a divorce between two Christians.

I remember asking the Lord, "Did I miss your message, Lord? Were you telling me to confront her?" I was heartsick. Could tragedy have been averted? Perhaps not. Nevertheless, I am less naive today. If that were to happen again, I hope I would have the courage to say to her, because I know her well, "Ann, when I saw you talking to Al, you looked very close. Perhaps I misinterpreted what I saw, but it didn't look right to me. I feel I need to tell you that." What's your response to this kind of confrontation?

(Notice the "perhaps I misinterpreted. . . . " It is imperative to remember that you could be totally wrong.) How would you respond if someone confronted you in that way?

8. In his bestselling book *The Road Less Traveled,* Scott Peck makes this observation: "To fail to confront when confrontation is required for the nurture of spiritual growth represents a failure to love equally as much as thoughtless criticism or condemnation. . . ."[1]

**Discuss in your group: What is your response to Peck's idea that it is as unloving to not confront when needed as it is to criticize and condemn?**

9. One more Scripture we need to look at: James 5:19, 20. What are the results of "bringing someone back"?

Does anyone come to mind that you might be able to help "bring back"? If appropriate, share your concern with your group.

**Close your time together in a time of sentence prayers, those who wish to do so, praying for God to purify His people, and for ourselves to be willing to be purified. Also ask to be alert to the leading of God to confront others.**

[1]Peck, M. Scott, *The Road Less Traveled* (New York: Simon and Schuster, 1978), p. 153.

# 6. Without God It Won't Work

*Icebreaker Idea: Have everyone share one way that life on earth would be different if there were no gravity for one minute every day at noon. Without gravity (even for one minute each day) life could get pretty absurd. In the same way, we need to rely on God if our relationships are to live up to their fullest potential.*

I started this book by acknowledging how difficult it is for us to have successful relationships. For example, the more I've learned about communication, the more I believe it is a "miracle" when any two people in a close relationship can actually understand one another, especially about issues on which they disagree or have strong feelings. Each of us brings his or her own baggage of hidden expectations, a tendency to misperceive messages, and our fears.

Acceptance—true, deep acceptance of another human being who is so different from me—that too, I believe is a "miracle." It can't be done, at least not by me, apart from the life of Jesus Christ living in me.

I am increasingly convinced that it takes God to enable us to reach our potential in any relationship. Being a believer in Jesus Christ must make a difference in how I relate. If not, my Christianity is a sham. John 13:35 quotes Jesus, saying, "All men will know that you are my disciples if you love one another." Of course, some unbelievers are much more effective relaters and more loving than some believers. There's no doubt about that. But it's not fair to compare John the believer with Joe the unbeliever. We must compare Joe *before* he became a Christian with himself *after* he became a Christian, and the same with John. Then we can truly see the difference that Christ has made in the way that each relates to others.

**Discuss in your group: What is your response to my idea that some people who do not have Christ in their lives may be more loving and better relaters than some believers?**

What is a "believer"?

**Take a moment to make sure you all understand how a person becomes a believer in Christ. (Your facilitator may want to distribute a booklet such as "The Four Spiritual Laws," "How to Have a Happy and Meaningful Life," or "Steps to Peace With God."**

**Addresses where these can be obtained are in the introductory section of this book. Your local Christian bookstore may have them on hand.)**

What differences has Christ made in the way you relate to other people?

If you became a Christian as an adult, what differences did you notice in the way you treated others after you became a Christian?

**Talk together about the interpersonal dynamics in your group. What are some ways the relationships in this group have demonstrated to you the life of God in one another? Give each other some specific "warm fuzzies."**

**Example: "Ellen, I have especially liked the way you called me to see how things were going with that concern I shared in the group. I felt cared for."**

**Or: "Carl, even though it was painful, I appreciated your telling me how you thought my husband would be feeling if I took the action I shared here. I could see it was hard for you to confront me like that. You helped me. I thank you."**

1. There are many ways we can liberate the power of God in our relationships. Let's cover two ways: prayer,

and solitude. What do you think I mean by "liberate the power of God"?

What is the opposite of His power being free in our relationships?

What do we do that limits His freedom to change us? (There are many answers to this question.)

## Choosing to Pray

2. Two ways that God can work to transform our relationships are by transforming us through prayer and through solitude. First, prayer. Let's look at one of the main concerns on the heart of the Lord Jesus as He looked ahead to leaving His disciples. What was His request to the Father for them in John 17:11, 23?

### Read I John 3:23.

What is the command of God?

In these Scriptures we see how important unity is to God, and we see Jesus praying for that.

3. When and how often do you pray specifically for the people in your life with whom you have tensions, so that unity can come?

How do you think you should pray? For what?

A friend of mine teaches in a large school system where there is little district supervision of administrators. The principal in her school has an obvious drinking problem. As a result, the school is disorderly, a difficult place to maintain the best learning environment. My friend has felt very resentful of this man, because his failures were making her life more difficult. Recently she began praying for him, not just as the principal, but for him as a human being, for his personal needs, for him to get help with his alcoholism. What result do you think she noticed first? Her own attitude toward him changed markedly.

What experience have you had in praying for someone toward whom you feel resentful? What were the results?

What do you think stops us from praying for those toward whom we feel resentment?

The apostle Paul frequently modeled praying for others. His specific requests are written out for us in his letters. Have you ever prayed a scriptural prayer (using the actual words of Scripture) regularly for anyone?

**Share any experiences you've had in this area.**

I have used Colossians 1:9-11 to pray for each member of my family and my close friends. Read that passage.

(name) with the knowledge of your will through all spiritual wisdom and understanding. I pray this in order that she may live a life worthy of you and please you in every way. I pray that she will bear fruit in every good work, and grow in the knowledge of God, being strengthened with all power according to your glorious might, so that she will have great endurance and patience, and be a joyful giver of thanks to you, Father."

If every Christian parent prayed this for his or her children, imagine the tension that would be prevented and the godliness that would result. If you have children, how do you pray for them?

**Share your experiences with the group.**

**Have someone read II Timothy 2:25, 26.**

I have used this passage to pray for someone attending a program I ran, who was very argumentative about spiritual things. The results have been unbelievable. Others have noticed the change in this person. The power of God freed by the prayer has been a vital part of that process of change.

Here's the prayer: "Lord, grant (name) repentance leading him to a knowledge of the truth. I pray that he will come to his senses and escape from the trap of the devil. I ask you to make him a man of God who does your will."

How do you pray for relatives or friends in your life who seem to be hostile to spiritual things?

4. What specific requests does Paul make for others in these passages?

- II Corinthians 13:7


- Colossians 1:9-11


- Ephesians 1:18


- I Thessalonians 3:10-13


**Ask for two volunteers, one to pray and one to be prayed for, using Ephesians 3:16-19. Personalize that prayer with the person's name as illustrated in #3.**

5. If you are writing in your answers, before or after the group meeting write that prayer here, praying it for someone you love:




6. In my opinion, all of us have a difficult time maintaining an effective prayer life. Why do you think that is? What keeps us from praying?

Stop for a moment and go around your group, each of you sharing one need you have in regard to becoming more effective in your prayer life.

Now spend a few minutes praying for one another, that we each will choose to make prayer a priority.

◆

## Choosing Solitude

7. The second way that I believe we can affect our relationships in a spiritual way is through solitude. That probably sounds strange to you. We can be better relaters by spending time alone? What do you think of that idea?

We are a treadmill society. And we find it difficult to get away and be quiet. Furthermore, we don't know what to do when we are quiet and alone. I think solitude is scary to the average American. Let's explore our feelings and attitudes toward solitude.

What does the word "solitude" mean to you?

What feeling do you have when you think of yourself experiencing solitude?

8. The definition I'm using for "solitude" is "time alone, spent in quiet with myself and with God." Out

of solitude comes an inner state of peace and genuine caring for others. Being with the Father does that for you.

**Read Mark 1:32-39.**

What was happening before and after Jesus "went off to a solitary place, where He prayed?"

What do you think it was like to have people clamoring after you for help and healing, to have "everyone looking for you" (vs. 37)?

How do you feel when you are in that situation of many people making demands on you or needing you?

I feel depleted, and if I don't get alone with the Lord and with myself, I begin to feel resentful. (For helpful information on relating to the Lord and to yourself, see chapters 1 through 4 in my book entitled *Balancing Your Priorities: Living in Peace with God, Yourself, and Others* in this *Growing Together* series.

In a wonderful book by Henri Nouwen called *Out of Solitude,* the author says, "A life without a lonely place, that is, a life without a quiet center, easily becomes destructive."[1] What do you think he means? In what ways do you think you could become "destructive" when you have no "quiet center"?

How, specifically, do you think that a life without solitude contributes to tensions in relationships?


In commenting on the passage above, where Jesus went to a lonely place for prayer long before dawn, Henri Nouwen says this: "In the center of breathless activities we hear a restful breathing. Surrounded by hours of moving we find a moment of quiet stillness. In the heart of much involvement there are words of withdrawal. In the midst of action there is contemplation. And after much togetherness there is solitude. The more I read this nearly silent sentence locked in between the loud words of action, the more I have the sense that the secret of Jesus' ministry is hidden in that lonely place where He went to pray. . . ."[2]

To fully grasp the rich meaning of this paragraph, fill in the chart below with the contrasting words in this quote:

| Action of life and ministry | Solitude |
|---|---|
| 1. breathless activities | 1. restful breathing |
| 2. hours of moving | 2. |
| 3. | 3. |
| 4. | 4. |
| 5. | 5. |

What keeps you (you personally) from times of solitude?

In a book called *I Can, I Can, I Can If I Want To,* Arnold Lazarus gives this illustration: Think of something you think you can't do (such as find time for solitude), then ask yourself questions like these:

a. If someone offered you $10,000 to do what you say you can't do, would you do it?

b. If someone held a gun to the head of your closest loved one and he or she would be shot if you did not do what you say you cannot do, would you do it?[3]

Thought-provoking questions, aren't they? Let me ask you a couple more questions.

c. If you really believe you are going to account to God for your priorities, will you find time for quietness with Him? II Corinthians 5:10 makes it clear we are going to give an account. (Read this verse now.)

d. If you really believe He will give you a quietness and peace within that will affect the way you relate to others, will you find time for quietness with Him?

Spend a few minutes in silence thinking about this; then write a letter to the Lord about prayer and solitude in your life:

**Those who would like to may read their letters. Then spend some time in praying together to close this group.**

As a group, you may want to talk about the possibility of choosing another book to study together, or you may want to take a break for awhile.

Also, there may be someone in this group that you would like to have as a prayer partner. If that seems like a good possibility, approach that person and suggest you pray regularly together for a certain period, such as six months. At the end of that period, evaluate whether you want to continue or whether praying together has served its purpose and is completed.

It is my vision and prayer that working through this study will improve and enrich your relationships. I have loved sharing my thoughts and feelings with you.

(Facilitator: If you are using the 13-week method, see the introductory chapter to plan next week's session. You may want to contact volunteers to do summaries of each chapter.)

[1]Nouwen, Henri, *Out of Solitude* (Notre Dame, IN: Ave Maria Press, 1974), p. 21.
[2]Nouwen, pp. 13, 14.
[3]Lazarus, Arnold, and Alan Jay, *I Can, I Can, I Can If I Want To* (New York: Warner Books, 1975), p. 44.